guitar for everyone

G000149199

'first steps'
by marc ongley

Published by: **Natural Light Publications Limited**
41 Cloister Close, Teddington,
Middlesex, TW11 9ND
UK
email: sales@naturallightpublications.wanadoo.co.uk
web: www.guitarteachingbooks.co.uk

Order Ref. **NLPGFE-04**

ISBN: **0-9542802-4-5**
ISMN: **M 9002063 4 3**

Distributors:
For a full list of our International Agents see:
www.guitarteachingbooks.co.uk

Illustrations and cover artwork by Claire Tindall
Models: Hayley Blacklock, Frances Israel
Text photos by Marc Ongley
Book design and audio recording by Marc Ongley

About this book:
Natural Light Publications takes great care in ensuring that
every book and CD is manufactured to the highest standards
for your enjoyment and learning pleasure.

Printed by Halstan & Co. Ltd, Amersham, Bucks, England

Natural Light Publications Limited

a note to parents and teachers

This book is intended for very young students who have a teacher. It is important to work through this book slowly and to make sure the child is absolutely confident with each piece before moving on. Regular revision will help the young student gain confidence and make the whole learning experience more productive and enjoyable. It is recommended that the parent sit with their child during practice sessions at home and ideally the parent will learn along with their child. Regular practice is the key to success and it is recommended the young student begins with about five minutes practice each day. Practice times can be built up slowly - the important thing is that the young musician enjoys the whole process of learning - music is for pleasure.

contents

bits 'n' pieces of the guitar

CD TRACK 1

ask your teacher to show you how to tune your guitar to CD track 1 - all audio tracks can be downloaded for free from:
www.guitarteachingbooks.co.uk/firststepsaudio.html

frets (different notes are made by stopping the strings at different frets)

head

tuning keys (turning the key away from you makes the string sound higher)

nut (strings go over here and are tied on to the the tuning pegs)

strings (the thickest string is closest to you and is called the 6th string)

fretboard

neck

body

soundhole (some sound comes from here)

top or soundboard (some sound comes from here)

saddle (the strings go over here)

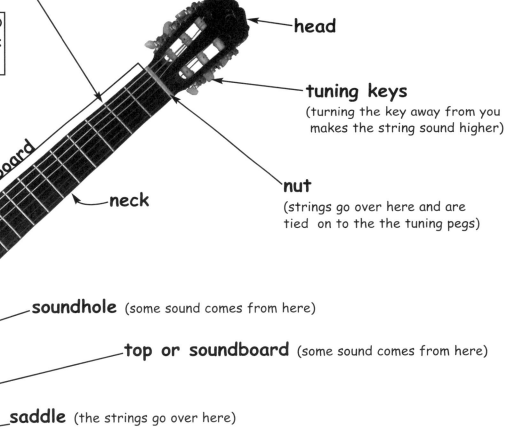

the plectrum (this plastic object can be used to strike the strings)

left hand fingers (the left hand fingers stop the strings to make different notes)

right hand fingers (the right hand fingers can be used to strike the strings)

bridge (the strings are tied on here)

Preparing For Your First Musical Steps

Left Hand

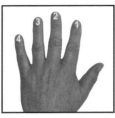

Right Hand

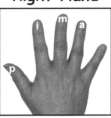

The Plectrum

Sitting Position - Plectrum

Sitting Position - Fingerstyle

The Note 'E'

The Note 'B'

The Note 'G'

'E' Open 1st String   'B' Open 2nd String   'G' Open 3rd String

Note Values

♩   'Crotchet' lasts for 1 count

♩   'Minim' lasts for 2 counts

𝅝   'Semibreve' lasts for 4 counts

Your first exercise playing and counting the note 'E'

Student

Count | 1   2   1   2   1   2   1   2

Teacher

By playing each day you will learn to make music and have a lot of fun doing it.

Let's Play 'E'

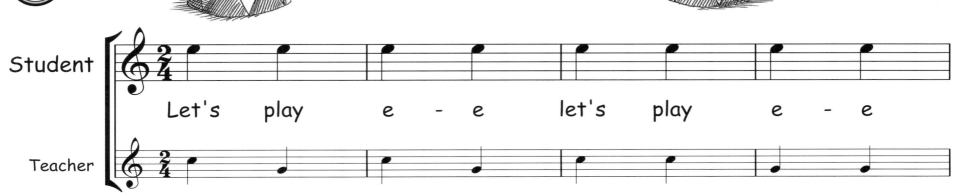

Student: Let's play e - e let's play e - e

Teacher: (accompaniment)

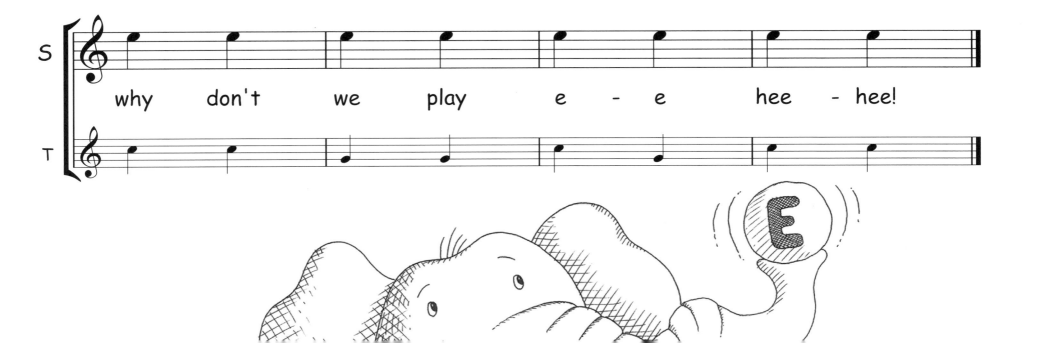

S: why don't we play e - e hee - hee!

T: (accompaniment)

My Little Teapot

CD TRACK 3

Student

My lit-tle tea pot. (2 3 4) Lit-tle tea pot hot. (2 3 4)

Teacher

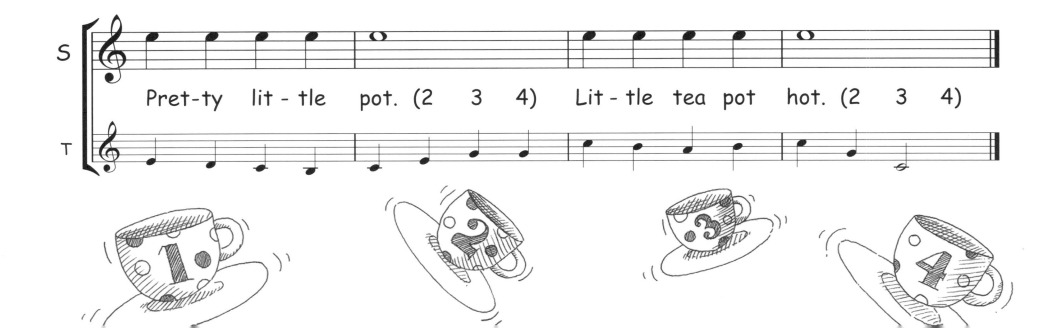

S

Pret-ty lit-tle pot. (2 3 4) Lit-tle tea pot hot. (2 3 4)

T

Let Us Play Some More

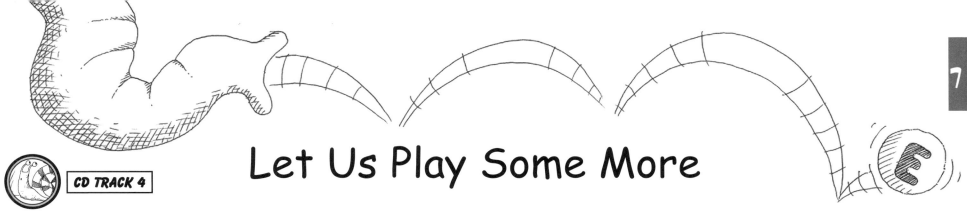

CD TRACK 4

Student

My friend's come to play with me. Hear the knock-ing at the door.

Teacher

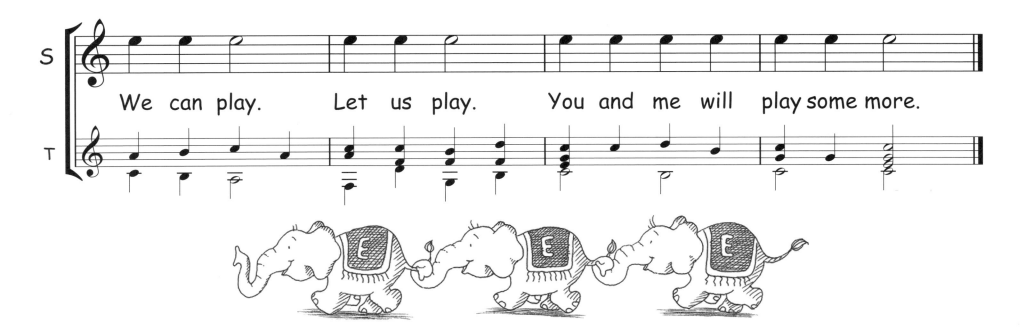

S

We can play. Let us play. You and me will play some more.

T

Jingle Jangle

CD TRACK 5

Student: Jin - gle jan - gle goes the bell. Can you hear it? Can you

Teacher

S: tell? Jin-gle jan-gle ding-a - ling I can hear a small bell ring.

T

CD TRACK 6

Waltzing

'Dotted minim' lasts for 3 counts

Student — Teach me to dance. Can you do that?

Teacher

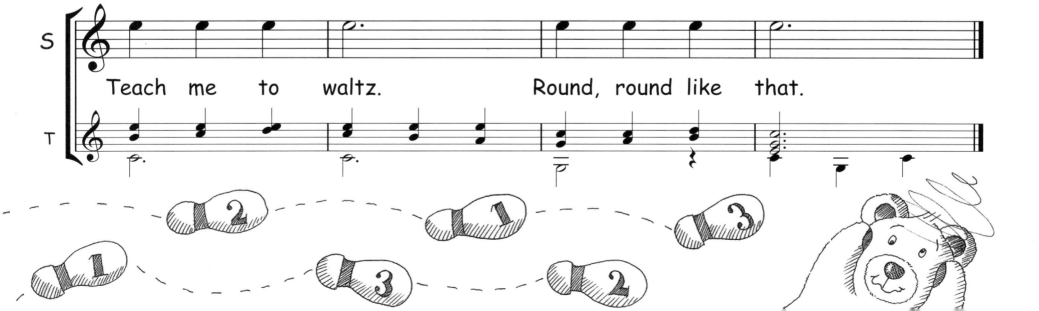

S — Teach me to waltz. Round, round like that.

T

 is a Treble Clef.

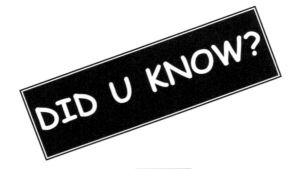

is a Stave.

is a Bar line.

Note Values

♩ is a crotchet. It lasts for 1 count.

𝅗𝅥 is a minim. It lasts for 2 counts.

𝅗𝅥. is a dotted minim. It lasts for 3 counts.

𝅝 is a semibreve. It lasts for 4 counts.

Time Signatures

$\frac{4}{4}$ means count 4 crotchet beats in each bar.

$\frac{3}{4}$ means count 3 crotchet beats in each bar.

$\frac{2}{4}$ means count 2 crotchet beats in each bar.

Clap and count

Don't count like this!   Do count like this!

Skipping

'B' Happy

CD TRACK 8

At a moderate speed

Student: 'B' 'B' Bee | hap-happ-y | I will 'B' | hap-happ-y

You will 'B' | hap-happ-y | We will both 'B' | hap-happ-y

Together With 'E-B'

Ellen & Barry's Waltz

At a moderate speed

Student

El - len and Bar - ry are dan - cing a waltz. (2 3)

Teacher

S

You can join in if you fan - cy, of course. (2 3)

T

CD TRACK 10

rhythm land

Counts

Add up the counts for each group of notes.

O   Answer = _____

Answer = _____

Answer = _____

Answer = _____

Time Signatures

Write the time signature $\frac{2}{4}$ $\frac{3}{4}$ or $\frac{4}{4}$ in the correct place and then add the counting under each bar as shown in this example.

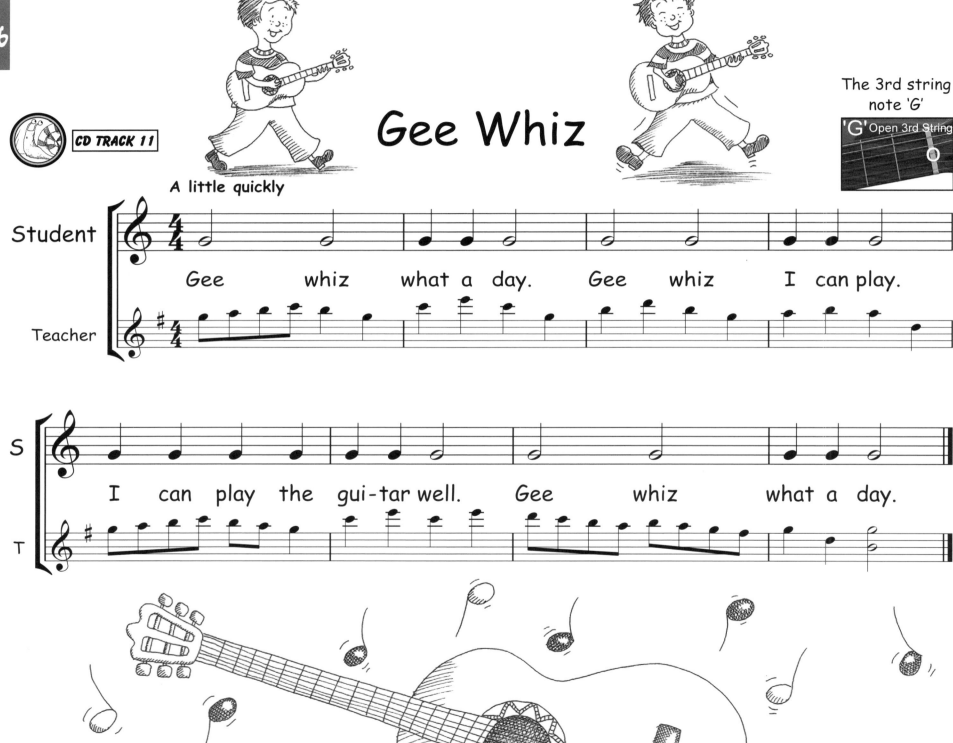

CD TRACK 11

Gee Whiz

The 3rd string note 'G'

'G' Open 3rd String

A little quickly

Student

Gee whiz what a day. Gee whiz I can play.

Teacher

S

I can play the gui-tar well. Gee whiz what a day.

T

I've Got The E-B-G-B's

CD TRACK 12

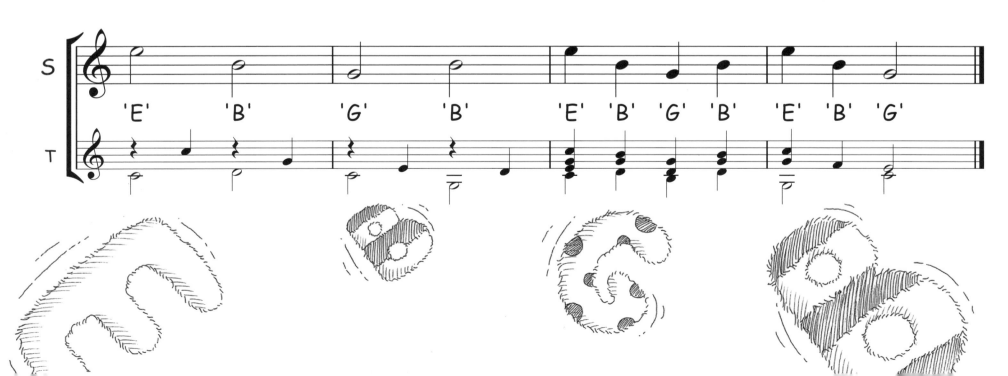

The Prowling Cat

CD TRACK 13

Slowly

Student / Teacher

Watch the prow-ling cat. Watch him as he waits.

Can he catch the big fat rat? Watch the prow-ling cat.

CD TRACK 14

The Weary Animals

A new note 'C'. Played with the 1st finger on the 1st fret of the 2nd string.

Slowly

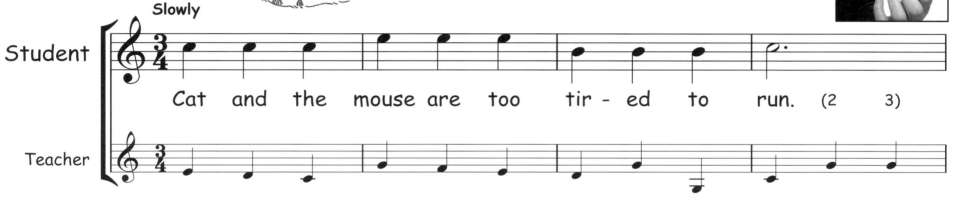

Student

Cat and the mouse are too tir - ed to run. (2 3)

Teacher

S

They are too wea - ry to have a - ny fun. (2 3)

T

CD TRACK 15

Let's Go To The Fair

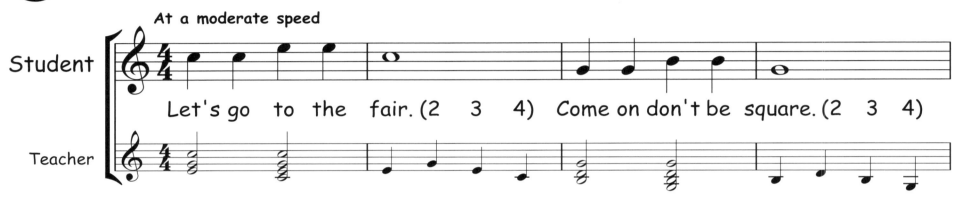

At a moderate speed

Student

Let's go to the fair. (2 3 4) Come on don't be square. (2 3 4)

Teacher

S

Let's go to the fair. (2 3 4) We will have fun there. (2 3 4)

T

CD TRACK 16

Best Friends

A new note 'F'. Played with the 1st finger on the 1st fret of the 1st string.

Student

Slowly

My   best   friends   please   come   to   tea.

Teacher

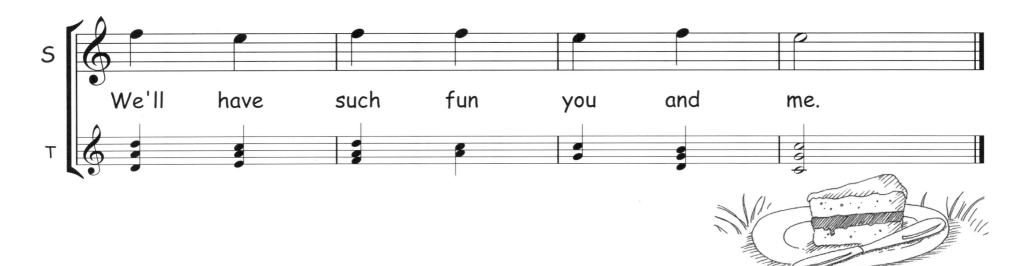

S

We'll   have   such   fun   you   and   me.

T

Time To Celebrate

CD TRACK 17

At a moderate speed

Student

Cel - e-brate the notes   we   now know in this book   yeah!

Teacher

S

I can now play   five notes 'F' - 'E' - 'C' - 'B' - 'G'   Look! (2   3   4)

T

What is this? _____

What is this? _____

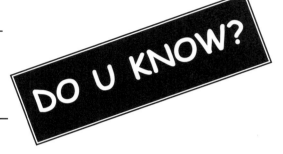

What is this? _____

Note Values

♩ This is a: _____ It lasts for: _____ count.

♩ This is a: _____ It lasts for: _____ counts.

♩. This is a: _____ It lasts for: _____ counts.

o This is a: _____ It lasts for: _____ counts.

Time Signatures

$\frac{4}{4}$ Means? _____

$\frac{3}{4}$ Means? _____

$\frac{2}{4}$ Means? _____

Note Names

Write out the names of each note on the line below.

A new note 'D'. Played with the 3rd finger on the 3rd fret of the 2nd string.

A new note 'G'. Played with the 3rd finger on the 3rd fret of the 1st string.

CD TRACK 18

Go Tell Aunt Nancy

Student

Teacher

Go   tell Aunt Nan - cy,   go   tell Aunt Na - an - cy,

S

T

go   tell Aunt Nan - cy the   old grey goose is   gone.

Hot Cross Buns

Fast

Student

Hot   cross   buns.   Hot   cross   buns.

Teacher

S

One a pen - ny two a pen - ny hot cross buns.

T

Gregory's Chant

CD TRACK 20

At a walking pace

Student

This is a ve - ry old song, long time 'go.

Teacher

S

Sing a - long with me my friend, just like so.

T

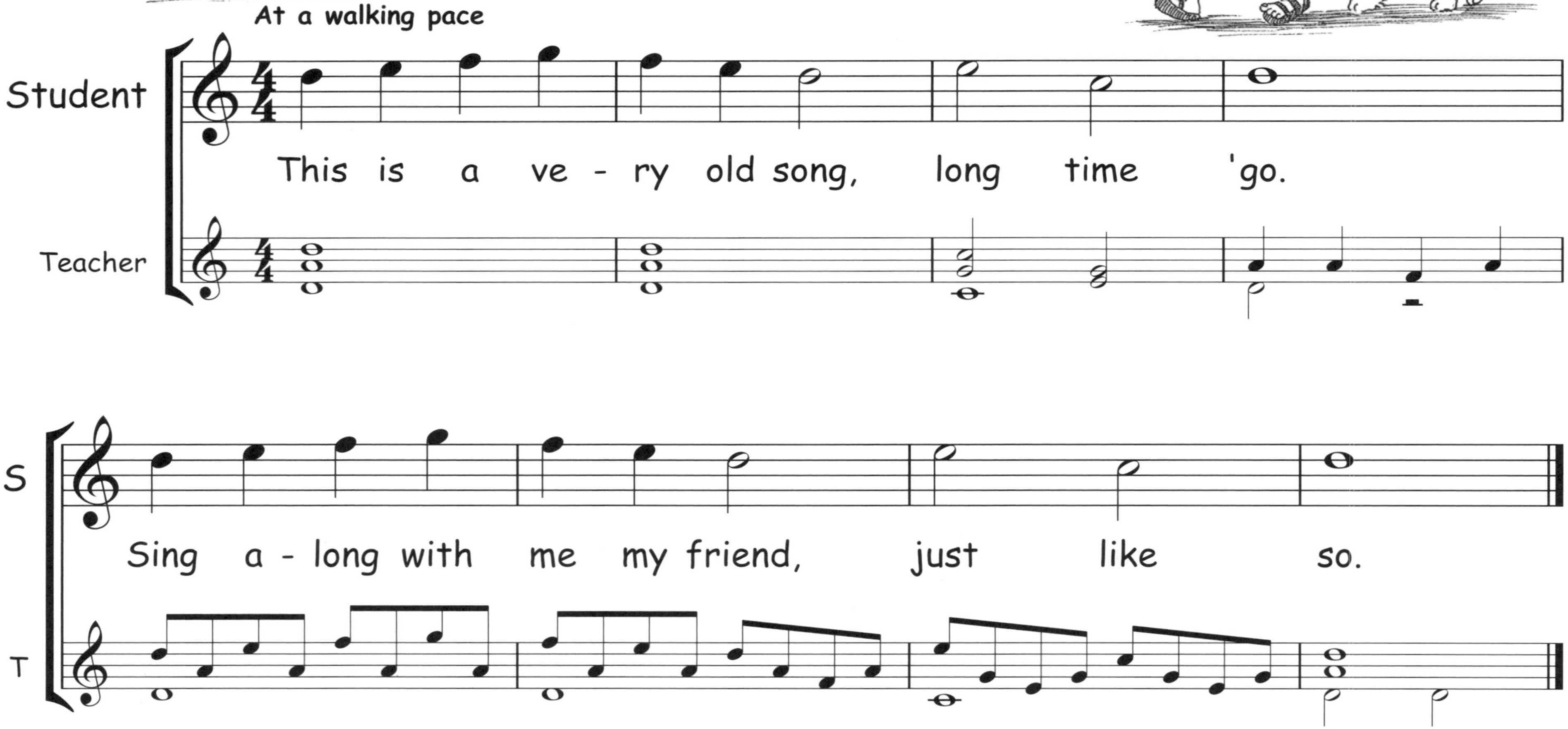

CD TRACK 21

Mary Had A Little Lamb

Quickly

Student

Ma - ry   had   a   lit - tle lamb,   lit - tle lamb,   lit - tle lamb,

Teacher

S

Ma - ry   had   a   lit - tle lamb   its   fleece was white as   snow.

T

CD TRACK 22

A new note 'A'. Played with the 2nd finger on the 2nd fret of the 3rd string.

Old MacDonald

At a moderate speed

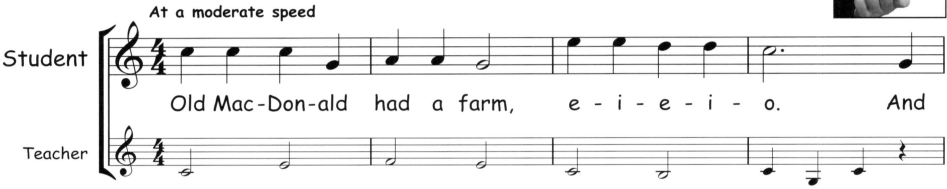

Old Mac-Don-ald   had   a   farm,   e - i - e - i - o.   And

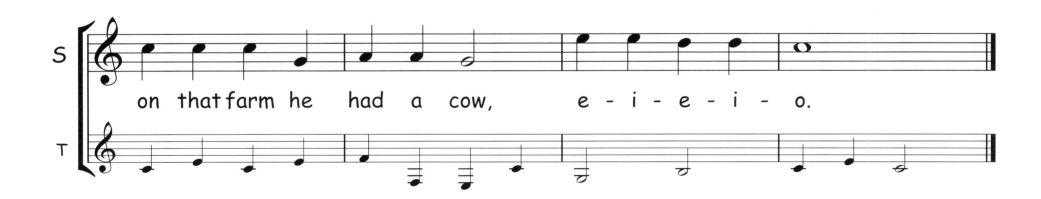

on that farm he   had   a   cow,   e - i - e - i - o.

This Old Man

A little quickly

Student

Teacher

This old man, he played one, he played nick-nack on my drum.

With a

S

nick - nack pad - dy - wack, give a dog a bone.

This old man came roll-ing home.

T

let's learn some chords

C chord
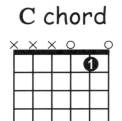

G chord
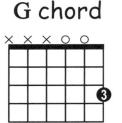

G⁷ chord
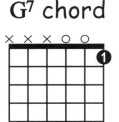

strum the top three strings with the plectrum or the right hand thumb to play each chord.

Chords to Mary Had A Little Lamb

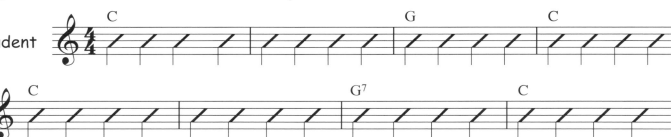

give four even strums to each bar and change chords when you see a new chord symbol.

Chords to Hot Cross Buns

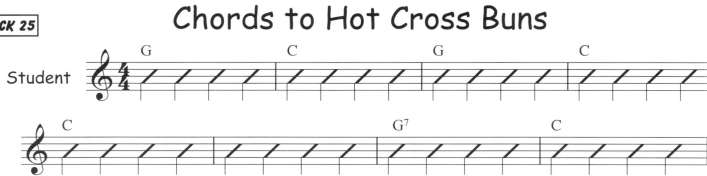

 Treble Clef.

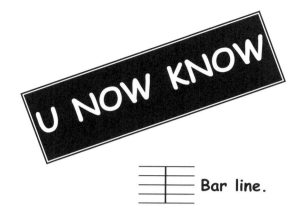

Stave.

Bar line.

Note Values

♩ Crotchet. It lasts for 1 count.

♩ Minim. It lasts for 2 counts.

♩. Dotted minim. It lasts for 3 counts.

𝅝 Semibreve. It lasts for 4 counts.

Time Signatures

$\frac{4}{4}$ Count 4 crotchet beats in each bar.

$\frac{3}{4}$ Count 3 crotchet beats in each bar.

$\frac{2}{4}$ Count 2 crotchet beats in each bar.

You learnt all these notes

You learnt these three chords

C chord   G chord   G⁷ chord

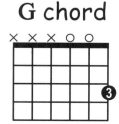

Well Done!

This certifies that

_____

has successfully completed the
Guitar For Everyone 'first Steps' guitar course.

_____ Teacher

_____ Date